ORFF ORCHESTRATIONS

GRADE 5

SERIES AUTHORS

Judy Bond

René Boyer

Margaret Campbelle-Holman

Emily Crocker

Marilyn C. Davidson

Robert de Frece

Virginia Ebinger

Mary Goetze

Betsy M. Henderson

John Jacobson

Michael Jothen

Chris Judah-Lauder

Carol King

Vincent P. Lawrence

Ellen McCullough-Brabson

Janet McMillion

Nancy L.T. Miller

Ivy Rawlins

Susan Snyder

Gilberto D. Soto

Kodály Contributing Consultant
Sr. Lorna Zemke

Macmillan
McGraw-Hill

ACKNOWLEDGMENTS

Grateful acknowledgment is given to the following authors, composers, and publishers. Every effort has been made to trace the ownership of all copyrighted material and to secure the necessary permissions to reprint these selections. In the case of some selections for which acknowledgment is not given, extensive research has failed to locate the copyright holders.

Uncle Pen, Words and Music by Bill Monroe. Copyright © 1951 by Unichappell Music Inc. Copyright Renewed. International Copyright Secured. All Rights Reserved.

Every Day I Have the Blues, Words and Music by Peter Chatman. Copyright © 1952 (Renewed) by Arc Music Corporation (BMI), Fort Knox Music Inc. and Trio Music Company, Inc. International Copyright Secured. All Rights Reserved. Used by Permission.

Macmillan/McGraw-Hill School Division
2 Penn Plaza
New York, New York 10121

Printed in the United States of America
ISBN: 0-02-295868-1

3 4 5 6 7 8 9 045 06 05 04

Table of Contents

Introduction

The Orff approach to music education actively involves students in speech, movement, singing, instrument playing, and drama. Developed by the German composer Carl Orff (1895–1982), the approach is based on the instinctive learning behavior of children. Improvisation and movement permeate the learning process, and the use of specially designed Orff instruments enables children to create and perform ensemble music at every level.

The materials used include both folk and composed music, along with chants, rhymes, and poetry. As students experience this music, they develop a musical vocabulary and skills that may then be used to create original works.

Orff orchestrations have been created for selected songs in SPOTLIGHT ON MUSIC. Along with each orchestration are teaching suggestions. The teaching suggestions include:

Instrumentation—All parts except timpani are commonly written in the treble clef. Bass xylophone and bass metallophone sound an octave below the written pitch. Soprano xylophone, soprano metallophone, and alto glockenspiel sound an octave above the written pitch. The soprano glockenspiel sounds two octaves above the written pitch. The alto xylophone and alto metallophone sound at the written pitch.

Teaching the Orchestration—A suggested basic teaching sequence is given for each orchestration. In orchestrations, the bass part is usually the most important. Students must be secure with this part before other parts are added. Except for the bass pattern, most parts may be considered optional. The teacher may choose to use only some of the suggested orchestration depending on circumstances—such as ability of students, time available, or the accessibility of specific instruments. Many of the arrangements can be musically satisfying with only the bass part and one other part added for tone color and/or rhythmic interest.

Form—Suggestions for the final form may include introductions, interludes, codas, chants, and opportunities for improvisation.

Noteworthy—This is a list of important musical elements that can be reinforced with the orchestration.

The Orff approach can infuse music classes with a spirit of cooperation and joy, enabling students to develop concentration and perception skills, increased aesthetic awareness and physical coordination, and a high level of motivation.

General Suggestions

1. Teach one pattern at a time. Allow students to take their time in learning each part. They should feel comfortable with singing the song while playing a pattern before adding the next pattern.

2. Teach each pattern through movement, with the song. Have students:

   • Mirror you in doing each new rhythm pattern with body movement—preferably large locomotor movements (walking, jumping)—especially for parts that occur on the beat and/or the strong beat. Others can be done with body percussion patterns you create (clapping, patting and/or stamping) or mirroring you in doing the movements required to play the part on the instrument.

   • Sing the song, doing the pattern in movement.

   • Remove any unused bars on pitched instruments, to make understanding and playing the patterns easier.

   • Form groups of three or four students around any available instruments and take turns playing the pattern. (Later, the pattern can be assigned to the instrument indicated in the score. At this time, you only want to give all the students an opportunity to learn the pattern and to help others in their groups to learn it.)

3. After teaching the most basic part, add other parts one at a time. Have students:

   • Sing the song, watching and listening as you play each new pattern.

   • Form two groups and sing the pitches or say the rhythm of the pattern while doing the pattern in body percussion (or by mirroring you) as the other group sings the song and plays previously learned patterns. Switch roles for the groups and repeat. (Use speech patterns given, or create your own. Patterns occurring only on the beat and strong beat, or on a single note—such as at the ends of phrases—can usually be taught without spoken patterns.)

   • All together, sing the song while doing the pattern in body percussion (or mirroring you).

Clarify pitches played, or learn about instrument technique as needed. Take turns playing the pattern while singing the song.

4. Relate the accompaniment to the lesson focus. Have students:

   • Recognize and describe ways that the accompaniment connects with and relates to the musical focus of the lesson. (It is important for students to realize what they are learning musically and how playing the accompaniments contributes to this.)

   • Review this connection each time you work on the orchestration.

5. Perform the accompaniment as indicated in the score, or as adapted by you and the students. Have students form groups at each instrument needed and take turns playing each part with the song.

In That Great Git'n Up Mornin'

Traditional Spiritual
Arranged by Marilyn Copeland Davidson

GRADE 5

In That Great Git'n Up Mornin' (page 2)

Amazing Grace

Traditional American Melody
Arranged by Judy Bond

Amazing Grace (page 2)

5

Uncle Pen

Words and Music by Bill Monroe
Arranged by Marilyn Copeland Davidson

Uncle Pen (page 2)

Uncle Pen (page 3)

Pen played the fid-dle oh, how it would ring,___ You could hear it talk,___ you could

hear it sing.

Opt. V. Slap

When Johnny Comes Marching Home

Words and Music by Patrick S. Gilmore
Arranged by Margaret Campbelle-Holman

When Johnny Comes Marching Home (page 2)

When Johnny Comes Marching Home (page 3)

When Johnny Comes Marching Home (page 4)

all   be   glad   when   John - ny   comes   march - ing   home.___

GRADE 5

The Caissons Go Rolling Along

Words and Music by Edmund L. Gruber
Arranged by Robert de Frece

The Caissons Go Rolling Along (page 2)

14

The Caissons Go Rolling Along (page 3)

Arirang

Korean Folk Song
English Words by Marilyn C. Davidson
Arranged by Soojin Kim Ritterling

English: A - ri - rang, A - ri - rang, A - ra - ri - yo.

You   are go - ing far a - way   o - ver A   -   ri - rang   hill.

Arirang (page 3)

Oh,   my   friend,   if   you   leave   me___ here a - lone,_____ may your

Arirang (page 4)

feet be - gin to hurt be - fore you've e - ven walked the first mile!

Fung Yang Song

Chinese Folk Song
Arranged by Virginia Nylander Ebinger

English: Sing the Fung Yang song. Sing it loud and long. With drums and cym-bals we

GRADE 5

Fung Yang Song (page 2)

sing the Fung Yang song.　This is　a song we can　sing the whole day long.

Fung Yang Song (page 3)

Fung Yang Song (page 4)

Fung Yang Song (page 5)

drr piao, drr piao, drr piao drr piao piao drr piao ling tang piao yi piao.

GRADE 5

Allá en el rancho grande
(My Ranch)

Music by Emilio Uranga
Spanish Words by Juan del Moral
English Words by Bartley Costello
Arranged by Virginia Nylander Ebinger

Allá en el rancho grande (page 2)

Allá en el rancho grande (page 3)

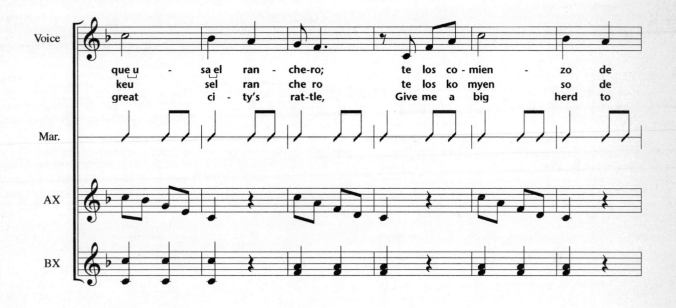

Voice: que u - sa el ran - che-ro; / te los co - mien - zo de
keu - sel ran che ro / te los ko myen so de
great ci - ty's rat-tle, / Give me a big herd to

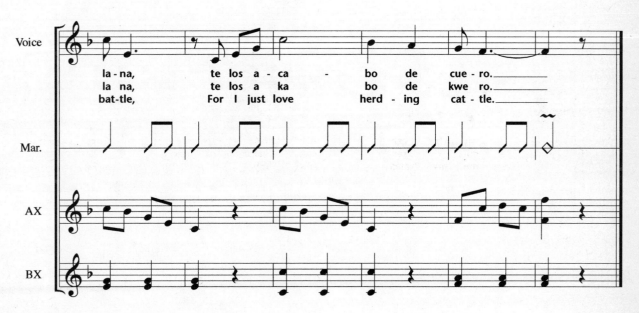

Voice: la - na, / te los a - ca - bo de cue - ro._____
la na, / te los a ka bo de kwe ro._____
bat-tle, / For I just love herd - ing cat - tle.

De colores
(Many Colors)

Spanish Folk Song
English Words by Jenny Wells Vincent
Arranged by Virginia Nylander Ebinger

Spanish: De_____ co - lo - res,_____ de co - lo - res se vis - ten los cam - pos en la pri - ma-

Pronunciation: De_____ ko - lo - res,_____ de ko - lo - res se vis - ten los kam - pos en la pri - ma-

English: De_____ co - lo - res,_____ man - y co - lors are all of the gar - dens and fields in the

GRADE 5

De colores (page 2)

De colores (page 3)

Voice

lo - res son los pa - ja - ri - tos que vie - nen de a - fue - ra._____
lo - res son los pa - xa - ri - tos ke vye - nen dea fwe - ra_____
co - lors are all of the birds - fly - ing in wing - time._____

Tri.

HD

SG/AG

SG/AG
(Opt.)

AX

AM/BM

De colores (page 4)

De colores (page 5)

De colores (page 6)

33

Mango Walk

Jamaican Calypso
Arranged by Jim Solomon

My moth-er deed-a tell me that you go man - go walk, you go man - go walk, you

go man - go walk. My moth-er deed-a tell me that you go man - go walk and

Mango Walk (page 2)

eat all the num - ber 'lev - en.

POP! Goes the Weasel

English Ring Game
Arranged by Nancy L.T. Miller

All a-round the cob-bler's bench, The mon-key chased the wea - sel. The

GRADE 5

POP! Goes the Weasel (page 2)

POP! Goes the Weasel (page 3)

pen - ny for a spool of thread, a pen - ny for a nee - dle,

POP! Goes the Weasel (page 4)

Goin' Home

Music by Antonin Dvorak (adapted)
Words by William Arms Fisher
Arranged by Robert de Frece

40

Goin' Home (page 2)

Goin' Home (page 3)

Voice

All the friends I knew, All the friends I knew.

AG/SM

BX

Bell Tree

F.Cym.

Bm

GRADE 5

Joshua Fit the Battle of Jericho

African American Spiritual
Arranged by Lauraine Williams-Bailey
and Marilyn Davidson

43

Joshua Fit the Battle of Jericho (page 2)

Joshua Fit the Battle of Jericho (page 3)

Joshua Fit the Battle of Jericho (page 4)

GRADE 5

Erie Canal

American Work Song
Arranged by Nancy Ferguson

Erie Canal (page 2)

Erie Canal (page 3)

al - ways know your pal, If you ev - er nav - i-gat - ed on the E - rie Ca - nal.

Mary Ann

West Indian Calypso

All day, all night, Miss Ma - ry Ann,

Mary Ann (page 2)

Down by the sea - shore sift - ing sand._____

Mary Ann (page 3)

E - ven lit - tle chil - dren join in the band_____

Mary Ann (page 4)

Down   by the sea - shore   sift - ing sand._____

Every Day I Have the Blues

Music and Words by Peter Chapman
Arranged by Judy Bond

Every Day I Have the Blues (page 2)

Melody

blues.   I   don't know why it's hap'-nin' 'cause I

AX/AM   (Improvise in F pentatonic)

S.Cym.
Tamb.
Bass Drum

BX

Melody

got   no   more to   lose.___

AX/AM   (Improvise in F pentatonic)

S.Cym.
Tamb.
Bass Drum

BX

Och Jungfrun Hon Går I Ringen
(A Girl with a Shiny Ribbon)

Swedish Dance Song
English Words by Linda Worsley
Arranged by Judy Bond

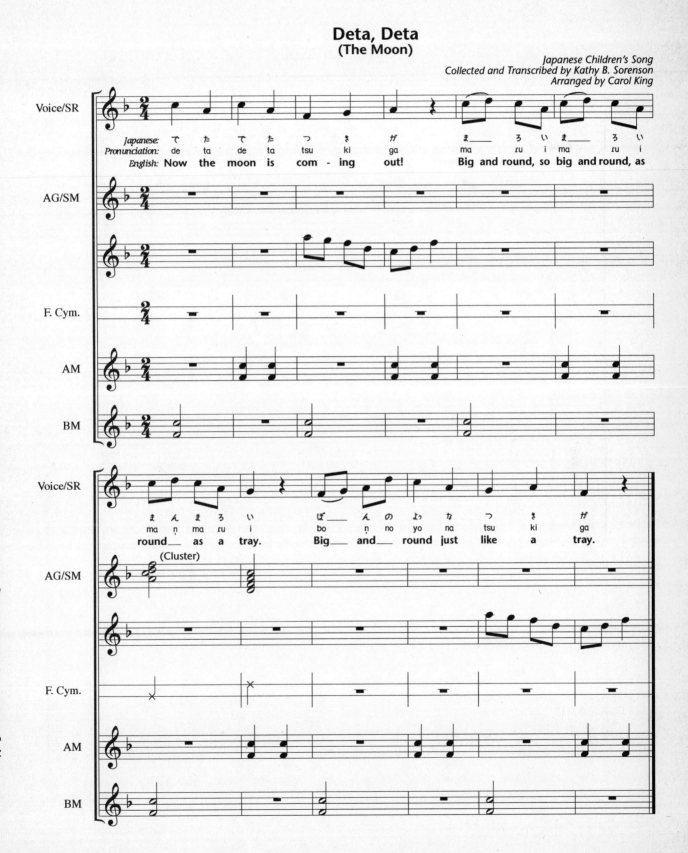

Hill an' Gully

Jamaican Calypso Music
Words by MMH
Arranged by Nancy Ferguson

Hill an' Gully (page 2)

Voice — Hill an' gul - ly ri - der, Hill an' gul - ly.

AG/SX

AX

Mar.

Guiro

Cowbl.
Bongo

BX

Hill an' Gully (page 3)

Voice — Rode my horse right down-town, Hill an' gul-ly. Wore a

GRADE 5

Hill an' Gully (page 4)

63

Hill an' Gully (page 5)

Somebody's Knockin' At Your Door

African American Spiritual
Arranged by René Boyer-Alexander

Somebody's Knockin' At Your Door (page 2)

66

La paloma se fue
(The Dove That Flew Away)

Puerto Rican Folk Song
Arranged by Alejandro Jimenez
English Version by MMH
Arranged by Marilyn Copeland Davidson

Has an - y - one seen him? The dove that flew a - way and left his home.

La paloma se fue (page 2)

He's gone, *la pa-lo-ma,* he's gone, *la pa-lo-ma,* He's gone, never to re - turn.

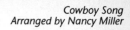

Streets of Laredo

Cowboy Song
Arranged by Nancy Miller

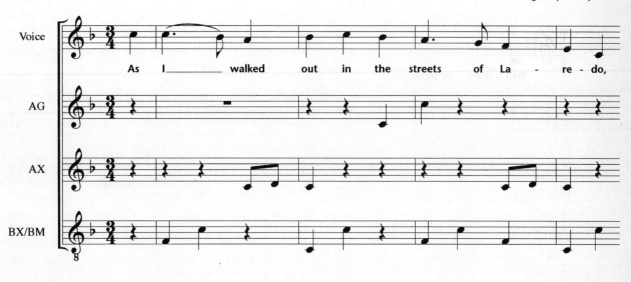

As I_____ walked out in the streets of La - re - do,

As I_____ walked out in La - re - do one day,

Los maizales
(The Cornfields)

Peruvian Folk Song
English Words by Linda Worsley
Arranged by Marilyn Copeland Davidson

De allacito carnavalito
(The Carnival Is Coming)

Argentine Folk Song
English Version by MMH
Arranged by Marilyn Copeland Davidson

Ev - 'ry-one there is___ com - ing down to the *car - na-va - li - to.*

GRADE 5

De allacito carnavalito (page 2)

Ev - 'ry-one comes down in cou - ples, I am a lone-ly__ so - lo.